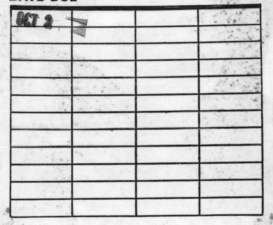

DATE DUE

OCT 2			

GRAINS OF PEPPER

GRAINS
OF
PEPPER

FOLKTALES FROM LIBERIA

Collected and edited by Edythe Rance Haskett

ILLUSTRATED BY MUSU MIATTA

The John Day Company

New York

*Dedicated to my dear friends
Vivian and Charles Sherman of Monrovia,
Liberia, whose love and friendship showed
me the warm heart of Liberia and its people.*

ACKNOWLEDGMENTS

For their assistance and cooperation in helping me gather these stories, I wish to thank especially the students of Episcopal High School, Robertsport, Liberia; and give particular thanks to Dr. Walter Murray and Dr. Betty Warner Dietz of Brooklyn College for their guidance and encouragement.

CONTENTS

GRAINS OF PEPPER

Liberia — Land of Promise

"In coming to these shores of Africa, we indulged in the pleasing hope that we would be permitted to exercise and improve those faculties which impart to man his dignity; to nourish in our hearts the flame of honorable ambition; to cherish and indulge every human heart and to evince to all who despise, ridicule, and oppress our race, that we possess with them a common nature; and with them susceptible of equal refinement, and capable of equal advancement in all that adorns and dignifies man." Thus spoke the early Liberian settlers when forming their new commonwealth.

On the west coast of Africa, between Sierra Leone and Ivory Coast, lies the first independent African republic — Liberia, a small, beautiful country of 43,000 square miles with a population of about two million people. Its history is so interwoven with the American scene that Liberia is often referred to as "a little slice of America in an African setting."

In 1822, Jehudi Ashmun, an agent for the newly organized American Colonization Society, landed on what was then called the "Grain" or "Pepper" Coast. He brought with him thirty-three persons to join the survivors of the three previous attempts to form a permanent settlement for freed slaves in Africa.

Paul Cuffee, a wealthy American Negro shipowner, had sailed in 1811 in his own ship with a party of freed men to Freetown, in Sierra Leone. Then, in 1815, with a group of thirty-eight he set sail for the Grain Coast, but heavy financial difficulties caused this settlement venture to fail.

Ashmun and his group of colonists settled on what is now the mainland of Liberia. This new settlement was named "Christopolis," or "City of Christ." Later the name was changed to Monrovia, in honor of James Monroe, the fifth President of the United States.

All was not easy for the new settlers. The native kings resented them and missed no opportunity to terrorize and harass them. The tribesmen did not understand that the colonists, in their foreign clothes and with their different ways and language, were their displaced brothers. Consequently, there was much conflict and many bloody battles. In spite of the hostile elements of heat, humidity, heavy rains and fever, the village somehow managed to survive and grow into a town. Other branches of the Colonization Society sent groups and supplies for the new nation.

With the signing of many treaties and the purchase of land from the native kings, peace at last came to the land of "freedom and promise."

On July 26, 1847 (now celebrated as Independence Day), the people of Liberia adopted a constitution and a flag (eleven red and white stripes, a blue field and one white star) and declared their country a free, sovereign and independent state. Joseph Roberts, an American Negro of Norfolk, Virginia, was elected Liberia's first president. Since its founding, Liberia has not been occupied or governed by any foreign power, but has consistently held fast to the country's motto, "The love of Liberty brought us here."

Many things have greatly changed in Liberia since 1847. Monrovia, the capital, is now a modern, progressive, industrial city with all of the characteristics of any metropolitan area. But far from the noise of the cities, and far from the modern highways, the villagers pursue their daily routine in the same simple, unhurried manner as they did generations ago. It is here that we can hear the storyteller telling and retelling the legends and tales of the tribe and the country's early history. Some of the stories tell of great warriors, brave hunters, mighty kings and their kingdoms, crafty and clever animals and the vices and virtues of people. Many of the stories teach a moral lesson — truth, kindness, honesty, unselfishness and right doing. The audience ofttimes participates in the storytelling by thinking up endings for a story.

For the boys and girls of America who will find pride in the folklore of their ancestors, here are some of the Liberian tales that charmed and delighted me during my two wonderful years in Robertsport, Grand Cape Mount County, Liberia, West Africa.

EDYTHE RANCE HASKETT

GRAINS OF PEPPER

How a MAN Became Unwitched

Far in the land of the Gios, there lived a man who was called Keisoe. This Keisoe was having a hard time providing food for his family. Mr. Hungry stayed long in his house. For many days there was no rice in the bowls of Keisoe's wife and children. In a faraway time, Keisoe had known the secrets of "strong medicine," but someone had "witched" Keisoe's medicine power. His farm dried up. His children grew thin and lean. His goats and chickens died. Hard times sat long on Keisoe's back.

In another town, far from Gio land, there lived a "diviner" — a wise man who knew strong and powerful medicine. After a four-day walk across the mountains to the north, Keisoe reached the diviner. The wise man saw

Keisoe coming and begged him to come quickly, for he
had divined his trouble.

"O true and noble wise man, I come from the far land
of the Gios, the home of my father and the land of my
ancestors. Someone has 'witched' me, and my times are
bad. My crops are poor. My children sicken unto death.
My wife grows thin. My house is old and weak. I want
you to take this terrible 'witch' off me. This I beg of you,
O wise and noble one."

The wise man listened to him and said, "I will think
on your trouble. Tonight I will read the sands, and after
one moon I will tell you what to do. For now you must
bring me seven white kola nuts, seven mats and seven
chicken eggs."

On the morrow Keisoe brought all these things. The
wise man had given long consideration to all Keisoe told
him. "If a man lives in one place and hard times catch
him, he should leave and make his house in another
place." With those wise words, he gave Keisoe a cotton
tree seed and a long stick with a short-hooked limb at
one end. "Travel to a certain new place and maybe beyond. Drag this stick behind you. If it catches in a root,
rock or bush, and the stick 'jukes' you, then there is the
place you must make your house. You must bring your
wife and children and try for Good Fortune to sit in this
new house."

"Will my family be the only one in this new place?"
asked Keisoe. "This does not sit well in my stomach, old
man. My heart beats with fear with too much being
alone in this new place."

"Never mind," replied the old man. "This cotton tree seed will protect you. Guard it well and keep it close to you always, and Good Fortune will sit down in your house. Build your house strong, and live there with your wife and children. Your crops will be good and your children will grow fat."

With heavy heart and long face, Keisoe put his feet in the path that led to his village, dragging the stick behind him. He walked for four days to reach his family. They gathered their small, poor things and began their search for their new place.

On the fourth day, and in a certain place, the stick "juked" and hooked in the root of a big tree. "Ah-ha," cried Keisoe, "this is the place for true, for the wise man said the stick must hook, and here I must build my house."

His wife and children cut palm thatch, and Keisoe cut sticks for the new house. Next he planted a farm. For true, Good Fortune sat long in Keisoe's new house.

Many rains passed, and the children grew and married. They built other houses. Soon this new place was a village with people, goats, chickens and children around each house. The village grew into a town. Today that town is called Zuen, a part of the Boo-Quila chiefdom.

When Keisoe died, he was buried with the cotton tree seed in a bag around his neck. It was the same seed the diviner had given him many years ago. After many rains, a beautiful cotton tree grew from the grave. The people of the town of Zuen began to worship the tree, for they believed that the spirit of Keisoe lived in the tree.

Until this day the cotton tree is given great respect. No foreign tongue or dialect is spoken in its presence, and no respectful person will cut the cotton tree unless he exercises the proper medicine.

How Sima Humbugged a Crocodile

In a far town by the river, the men were so rich and lazy that they spent all their time gambling and playing cards. They played night and day, and even the animals joined their games. The work on the farms was done by the women and other lowly people.

A farmer whose name was Sima, seeking land to farm, came down the river in his canoe. With him he brought his one wife and baby girl. Near the river he built a house, and on the far side of the river he made his farm.

Sima cut down a big tree. Out of the tree he made a canoe for his wife and taught her to paddle it so she could bring him his food.

One day as his wife and child were crossing the river a crocodile grabbed them and carried them under the

water. Sima's food time came and went without any food
from his wife. So he thought she was sick and kept on
working his farm.

When he reached home after work, he didn't see the
second canoe or his wife and child. He searched all over
the town and far into the forest. He called her name, but
no answer. His heart was heavy with fear. He walked to
the river. There he saw a curious thing. A crocodile was
undressing himself! What a strange thing to see! A
crocodile hanging his skin on a tree!

This crocodile man set off for town to gamble and play
cards. As he strolled along he sang this song:

> Crocodiles are clever,
> Especially under water,
> Weaker beasts can never
> Catch a woman and her daughter.

As Sima looked at this strange sight, his mind turned
in and he became very suspicious. He tiptoed over to the
skin, and took it to his house, where he hid it in a good
place. Then, he went into town, where the gambling was
going on, and took a seat beside the crocodile.

The crocodile man called himself Mano and was very
good at games. As he threw the gambling sticks three
times in the air, he said as they fell, "I win as I won a
man's wife and daughter today."

"What do you mean?" Sima asked.

"I mean what I say. Let us play," replied Mano, the
crocodile man.

Sima took the gambling sticks and threw them into the air three times. As each one fell to the ground he said, "I win as I won a crocodile skin tonight."

"What did you say?" asked Mano.

"Nothing important. Let us play," said Sima.

Soon Mano hurried off to see if his skin was still on the tree. The skin was gone for sure. So he returned to the gambling place and asked Sima, "What do you know of my skin?"

"And what do you know of my wife and child," asked Sima. He took the gambling sticks and threw them three times in the air, and as they fell he sang this song:

> A crocodile is somewhat vile,
> To steal a woman and her child.
> I know well that such a sin,
> May cost that crocodile his skin.

Mano started wailing and moaning and offered to bring back Sima's wife and child. Off he went to get them. Sima gave him back his skin and his family was returned to him.

From that time on, no crocodile has ever humbugged people without paying a price. Some people say this is really true.

Catfish and His Terrible End

Catfish and Rice Bird were once good, good friends. One day as they sat talking, Rice Bird said, "I just saw a farmer cut a hole in the top of a palm wine tree to catch the wine in a bowl. Let us go and steal some."

"That would be nice," agreed Catfish. "I am tired of drinking water, but you know I cannot fly."

"I will lend you some of my feathers," said the Rice Bird. He gave Catfish almost half his feathers, and they managed to fly to the top of the palm wine tree. There they sat and drank much wine. They returned to the river, and Catfish gave the feathers back to Rice Bird. Every other day they would fly up to the palm wine tree and drink their stomachs full.

Now, there came a time when they drank too much wine and became very, very drunk — so drunk that they could barely move. While they were lying in the palm wine bowl, the owner of the wine came up the tree. Catfish and Rice Bird stopped their drunken singing and listened. The farmer climbed closer, screaming harsh words and shaking a big stick. Rice Bird became very frightened because he knew in his condition he could not fly. He hastily pulled his feathers from Catfish and flew away. Poor Catfish lay helplessly in the wine bowl, drunkenly crying, begging and protesting. The angry farmer found him there.

He was so surprised to find a catfish in his wine that he almost fell down the tree. He took Catfish out and carried him home. His wife built the fire and put on the pot to cook Catfish. As Catfish was cooking he sang this sad song:

> Sometimes a friend,
> Does not intend,
> To help one faithfully.
> Those with such friends,
> Will meet their ends,
> And terrible ends they will be,
> And terrible ends they will be.

Tola and the Sea Monster

Old, old men tell the story of a noble chief who had a very beautiful daughter whose name was Tola. She was beautiful, clever, and above all, she was her father's favorite daughter.

Now, the time had come for Tola to marry and practice all the wifely skills she had been taught, but Tola refused to marry any man with a scar or blemish on his skin.

Her father sent messengers to towns near and far, searching for a man without blemish. Many strong and noble men came — princes, chieftains, sons of chieftains, warriors, hunters and kingly born men — but all were turned away because of some small blemish on their skin.

Tola had a devoted brother who was just as ugly as she was beautiful. When it suited his wishes, this ugly brother would change himself into a fly, and spy on the young men who came seeking marriage with his sister.

Far away in the deep, deep sea lived a monster who had heard of Tola's great beauty, and he made up his mind to have her for his bride. His plan for winning the beautiful Tola was very clever. Using fine, sweet words, he borrowed the soft, smooth skin of the Sea Goddess. The skin fitted him very well, and no one would know that under the skin was the evil sea monster.

With a canoe filled with diamonds, pearls, gold and pretty shells, he journeyed to Tola's home. He was received by her father, who noted the rich gifts but made no agreement before Tola had seen the young "man."

When Tola heard that another rich and handsome man had come seeking marriage, she sent her brother (as a fly) to see if this stranger had spots, sores or birthmarks on his body.

Her brother found the stranger dressing himself in beautiful robes embroidered with much gold and rubbing himself with sweet-smelling oil.

The "fly" buzzed around the stranger, searching his legs, neck, arms, stomach, back and chest for even a tiny, tiny spot that might not be seen through his clothes, but the skin the monster had borrowed from the Sea Goddess was as smooth as silk. So the ugly brother (who was the fly) went to report his findings to his sister.

"O sister," he announced, "this stranger's skin is most

fine. It is most wonderfully smooth and soft. It is beautiful beyond any man's."

"Then I shall marry him," exclaimed the sister. No one
suspected it, but this ugly brother was wise beyond his
years. He felt that this stranger was "too perfect." So he
said to his sister, "Beloved sister, take care, and take
time, for there is a badness about this stranger that I do
not like."

"Hold your tongue," commanded his sister. "You are
jealous of the stranger's fine looks and his great wealth.
I will marry this handsome man and go with him to his
town."

The brother knew his sister wanted very much to
marry, so he said nothing more, but he pondered many
things in his heart. For all of his sister's big talk, she had
not yet seen the stranger.

The monster from the sea entered the chief's house
and presented his plea for marriage with many gifts.
With heavy heart the old man listened, for he knew the
foolish ideas of his daughter. At last he said, "My son, it
seems that you are a 'do-right' fellow, but my daughter
will give me much 'palaver' [argument]. She is a stub-
born, proud, disobedient girl. She causes me much pain,
for her marriage time is upon her and she will not make
up her mind."

At that moment Tola, straight as a palm and as beautiful as the Sheba queen, came into the room.

"Father, who is this man?" asked the proud girl.

"He is a prince from a distant land, my daughter, and he is seeking marriage with you."

When she saw how handsome the man really was, her heart grew soft with love for him. "Give me in marriage to him, Father, and I will seek no more." Happiness spread over the chief, and he embraced his daughter and the monster. He shouted to his messengers to proclaim a "Day of Days."

The town prepared a fine feast. Families and friends from near and far were invited to the festivities. For days and days there was dancing, music, feasting and rejoicing throughout the land. Many fine gifts of cloth, gold, food and beads were brought to the couple.

When the marriage ceremony was over, the monster "man" and his bride Tola left for the journey to the monster's home. They traveled overland, carried in hammocks, until they came to the sea. Here, at the water's edge, was the monster's canoe piled high with the wedding gifts. As Pa-Ma, the monster, began to paddle he sang:

> Pa-Ma is going, going, far away,
> Pa-Ma sing farewell, farewell, forever.

As the canoe moved swiftly out to sea, Tola sat happily thinking of her husband and her new home. When they were out of sight, the monster muttered some magic words, and the canoe went down to the Undersea World. There, on the bottom of the water, the monster took off the skin that belonged to the Sea Goddess. What a horrible sight! His body was covered with big green scales, and there were prickly fins sticking out of his back and neck. Tola was frightened out of her mind and tried to run away. The monster grabbed her and dragged her into a dark underwater cave. Tola yelled and screamed at the top of her voice, but no one heard her. Days and nights passed, but she did not know one from the other.

Musu-Ma, the monster's mother, looked on the child with sadness in her heart. "My child, you are kind and tenderhearted and so beautiful — What are you doing here?" she asked. "Why did you come? My son is evil and cruel. He has brought many girls here from faraway towns and has destroyed them all. I fear for you."

The poor, beautiful Tola cried and prayed for someone to come and take her away from the cruel monster, Pa-Ma.

Softly a fly buzzed close to her face. What was a fly doing in this dark underwater cave? At once Tola knew who it was. She looked up to brush the fly from her face, and there was her ugly little brother standing by her side.

"Brother, brother, my beloved brother, how did you get here?"

"Quiet!" he cautioned. "Don't waste time. I traveled with you in the canoe. I feared some evil might come to you. Look here, I have discovered the monster's magic box. Come quickly. The canoe is waiting."

Hand in hand they ran through the water to the canoe. Holding the monster's magic box in his hand, the brother

The sea monster dressed as a man
presented gifts to Tola's father

said certain magic words, and the canoe went swiftly over the sea to their home. They were received with great rejoicing and feasting by their father and the towns-people.

When Tola had recovered from the terrible experience, her father made a marriage agreement with Mambo, a great warrior from a neighboring village. Soon they were married.

Tola took her brother with her to her new home, and always kept him close to her house, for she would never forget his loyal kindness to her. Never again would she think of him as ugly, but only as a dear and loving brother.

The Dicot Tree and the Deer

Deer had a fine home in the forest close to the dicot tree. No grass grew under or near the tree. The ground was as clean and bare as a baby's body.

One day Deer looked down and saw her footmarks very clearly on the bare ground. This gave her great fear, for a hunter would surely follow her. So she said to the dicot tree, "Good friend, please cover my marks. Some hunter may see them and come to kill me." The dicot scorned the deer and sneered, "Whether you live or die is of no importance to me. Go and leave me."

"Then, so be it," sighed Deer. "But the thing that kills me will kill you too."

"You are foolish, Deer," said the Oweh bush nearby. "No hunter will come here."

"Men eat animals and cut down trees," said Deer. "If my footmarks betray me, then all of us will suffer."

For true, some days later, a hunter found the footmarks of Deer. He spied on her from a secret place until he knew her movements night and day.

On the third night, as she slept, the hunter killed Deer. He took the meat and skin back to town. The Chief received the hunter and his bountiful gift of deerskin and meat. "I thank you for this sweet meat and fine skin. Now I order a tree to be cut and a drum made for music and dancing."

"O, good and wise Chief," said the hunter, "there is a fine dicot tree at the place I killed the deer, and the wood of the dicot makes a fine drum."

"So be it," proclaimed the Chief. "Cut the dicot tree, for its wood has a pleasant tone."

When the woodcutters cut the dicot, they noticed the Oweh bush nearby and decided to cut it to use its rosin to rub the skin of the drum. So the bush and the tree were cut and taken to town. The tree was made into a drum, the deerskin was used to cover the drum, and the bush gave rosin to rub it. When the drum was beaten, you could hear the voices of Dicot, Deer and Oweh still quarreling. Listen to the drums — the quarrel even now goes on.

Think on Four Wives

Once upon a time, by the edge of the forest there lived three brothers who had seen many hard times. Hunger came often and stayed a long time with them.

One day the youngest brother said, "Let us go to the Chief and ask him if he will agree to give us anything we want for five days, and in return we will give him our real lives on the sixth day." All the brothers agreed to this plan.

Quick, quick, they went to the Chief and "talked the palaver" that was close to their hearts. The Chief listened and agreed to give each brother any one thing he wanted for five days, and on the sixth day he would take their lives. So the brothers made their decisions.

The oldest brother said, "Give me plenty of palm

wine," and for five days he drank wine until it was finished, and so was his life. The Chief took what was left
of his life and killed him.

The second brother asked the Chief to give him food.
For five days he ate and ate. His stomach was full to popping. When the Chief took his life on the sixth day, there
was only small life left, but the Chief took it anyway.

The youngest brother asked the Chief to give him
cloth. He had the cloth made into a beautiful robe. When
he put on the beautiful new robe, he was truly a handsome young man. Many young girls looked on him with
love in their eyes.

The Chief had a fine daughter, who was too beautiful
for ordinary men to look on, so the Chief kept her shut
up inside a tall fence. The youngest brother, who was
called Talwa, "dashed" the guards around the tall fence,
and on the fifth night went in and looked on the Chief's
daughter. These two beautiful people looked at each
other, and love came into their hearts. They talked much
soft, sweet talk. Later, when it was dark, they gathered
their things in a box and stole away into the forest.

In their haste to get away from the Chief, they brought
no food with them, and now hunger was hard upon
them. On and on they walked, and still there was nothing to eat in this part of the forest. They feared they
would die of hunger. From another path came a girl
with a basket of rice on her head.

"O lady, give us rice to eat. We are hungry too much,"
said Talwa. He offered her a piece of gold for two cups

of rice, but the girl refused it. Her eyes had turned to Talwa with great affection. "You are too, too fine, my man. Take my rice and eat, but let me be your wife or I will die of love for you," she said. Talwa took her as his second wife. The three of them cooked and ate the rice, and then traveled on.

The two wives and Talwa walked far into the bush and lost their way. They were almost dead from too much hard walking when they met another girl, who had come on a secret path through the forest.

"O maiden, lead us from this bush. We fear for our lives in this heavy forest," begged Talwa and offered her pretty cloth. She too looked on him with love in her eyes, and answered him, "I want no cloth, good friend. I will lead you from the bush if you will take me as your wife. If you do not, I will die of love, for my heart is full inside me." So Talwa took her for his third wife, and she led them out of the bush on her secret path.

Soon they came to a certain town, and there they slept. The Chief of this town did not like strangers, and any man who came was obliged to pass a test — if he failed he was killed. This was the test — The Chief had one hundred boxes of gold, and the question was: Which box did the Chief own when he was a young boy?

This Chief also had a daughter, who looked on the handsome Talwa with loving eyes, and because they agreed, Talwa took her for his fourth wife. This loving girl told Talwa which box belonged to her father when he was young.

The Chief called Talwa for the test. There before him were the one hundred boxes full of gold.

"Now choose," said the Chief, "or you will die."

Talwa walked closer and looked at the boxes, pretending to make magic signs. At last he pointed to a box and said, "This is the one. I know it is the one. I am not wrong. This is the box you owned when you were young."

The Chief was greatly surprised. For true, Talwa was right.

The Chief called his council together and told them, "For Talwa's cleverness, he will become a member of our tribe and will marry my daughter and share my lands."

And that's how it was that Talwa lived in that land with all four wives. And here is what each wife did for love of Talwa:

The first abandoned her family for him.

The second saved him from starvation.

The third saved him from dying in the bush.

The fourth saved him from having his head cut off.

Now the question is this: "Which wife did the most for him?

Talwa lived with his four wives in the new land

How Hare Asked for Wisdom

Hare went to Man and asked for much wisdom. "I am a small animal," he said, "and in the forest there are many animals larger than I and stronger than I. Therefore, I must have wisdom so that I can protect myself. I beg you give me this gift."

"I will see to it," said Man, "but you must do three things. The first thing you must do is to bring me two of Leopard's teeth dripping with blood."

"This I will do," agreed Hare, not knowing how he would accomplish this big thing.

The cunning mind of Hare told him to invite Leopard to his house for dinner. This he did. As they sat after dinner, Leopard yawned, showing his big white teeth. A clever idea came to Hare. He said, "You have very beau-

40

tiful teeth, Leopard. No other animal has teeth as fine as yours." These sweet words sounded fine to Leopard, so he opened his mouth wider. Hare took a big stick and hit Leopard in the mouth. Two teeth fell out. Hare grabbed them and ran to Man. With great pride he gave him the two teeth dripping with blood.

"Only a wise man could take two teeth from a living leopard and only a brave, strong man would even try," said Man. "Now the second thing you must do," continued Man, "is to bring me the most poisonous snake in the forest."

Hare agreed and rushed off to the bush and cut a long stick, putting small marks on it as he went along measuring animals.

The poisonous cassava snake saw Hare measuring animals and asked, "What are you doing, Hare?"

"I am measuring all the animals. Man has asked me to find out who is the longest animal in the forest."

"Measure me. I think I am the longest," bragged the snake.

Hare put his measuring stick beside the snake, and quickly he tied the snake to the stick at each end and in the middle. "You are the longest animal. Now I will take you to Man," said Hare.

"Welcome, Hare," said Man. "Only a wise man could have captured such a poisonous snake as this. You must do one more thing to obtain your request. Bring me all the little birds in the forest."

Hare built a fine, big cage and went to catch all the

little birds. This is how he did it — He whistled prettily
to the birds and told them, "Snake is going to eat all the
little birds he can find, and because I love you so much I
have made this big, strong house for you to sleep in where
Snake cannot humbug you. The foolish little birds flew
quickly into the cage. Hare fastened the cage and carried
it to Man.

Man thought on all the brave things that Hare had
done and said to him, "Hare, anyone who has as much
wisdom as you doesn't need any more. Therefore, I say
to you, go back to your place and never ask for wisdom.
Some people never know when they have enough."

The Clever Question

In a certain town far in the interior there lived a powerful and rich chief who had a very clever daughter. The wisdom and cleverness of the girl called Tua was known near and far. In that day it was most unusual for a girl child to read and write. Tua could not only read and decipher many great books, but she could also interpret dreams.

One day Chief Ozeku announced that any man who asked Tua a question which she could not answer would be given half of his chiefdom, but if Tua answered the question, then the man would die.

Many wise men asked serious and difficult questions of the clever Tua, but she answered with great ease, so the men were put to death.

By the river in this land lived an old woman and her
three sons. They were very poor, and many times their
stomachs were empty because there was no rice.

The oldest son said to his mother, "This hunger is too
hard for me to bear. I am going to the house of Chief
Ozeku and ask the clever Tua one big question that her
mind cannot answer."

"My son," said the mother, "think well before you go.
Many wise men have died and their questions thrown
back in their teeth."

He went against his mother's words and traveled to
Chief Ozeku's house. He received permission to ask Tua
this question: "What causes Negegboi, the yard snake, to
bite man?" The meaning of this question was this: What
is the cause of a man's bad fortune? Tua, without hesita-
tion, looked into the son's eyes and answered, "Nyim,
the black snake, hangs something on that man's throat."
This meant: A man is often betrayed by the loose tongue
of a friend.

So the oldest son's question was answered and he was
killed.

The second son prepared his journey to the house of
Chief Ozeku. This is the question he asked the wise Tua:
"Before God we are fools — what causes the vanity of
men?" Quickly Tua answered him, "Tintala, the cricket,
depends on heat to give the Bolon cry and all heat comes
from God." (The Bolon cry is a signal used by the Poro
Society.) Tua's answer meant: Man depends on emotion
when he brags, and man's emotions are made by God.

The second son's question was answered, so he was put to death.

Now the youngest of the three sons begged his mother to allow him to question Tua. Always her answer was "No. If you want to be killed, I would rather see you die before my own eyes. My heart is greatly troubled that you might die in a strange and distant land. Take care, my son, and sit here on your mat in the house of your mother."

Each day the young boy begged, and finally his mother agreed for him to go. Inside her heart she felt that he was going to die. "If you must go, then go, my son, but remember what happened to your brothers. I beg you to stay and let my old eyes rest happy with my son on his mat." The mother kept her tears hard in her eyes and made a big corn cake with strong poison inside. She gave it to him for food on his journey, for she would rather bury him herself than have him killed by other hands.

So the young son set out with his dog. When he came to the river, he sat down to wait for the ferry to take him across. He took out the corn cake his mother had baked for him and gave the dog a piece. The dog ate it and died. The boy looked on his dead dog's body and thought Is this an omen? If so, it seems to be an evil one. Straightway, he put the dog's body in the river. An eagle flew down and sat on the dead dog, and both of them floated down the river. The dead dog carrying the living bird was quite a sight to see. This sight gave the boy an idea for his question to Tua.

So this is the question he put to Tua: "Corn killed dog and the dead carry the living. What does this mean?" Tua consulted all her question books for three days, but she could not find the correct answer. At last she said, "I give up. You may go in and speak to my father."

And so it was that the third son's life was spared and he was given half of Chief Ozeku's chiefdom and Tua as his wife. The young man grieved for his brothers, but lived in peace and plenty with his clever wife Tua and his old mother, until she died.

Why Yams and Cassava Hide in the Ground

A long, long time ago, the people in the village of Kaneh thought yams and cassava were devils. No one ate or planted them — they didn't even dare touch them. Many of the village people had heard strange stories of yams dancing in the moonlight and cassava roots performing strange ceremonies after the sun was low in the sky. All the village people were curious about these strange doings, but nobody did anything about it.

The people of Kaneh always ate rice, greens, fish, and whatever meat the hunters killed. While there was plenty of food in the village there was happiness and laughter in every house, but after a long, long dry season, Hunger came and sat down in their town. The cooking pots were empty and the children's stomachs were hard and tight.

The evening fires were lit, but there was nothing to cook. The rice crop had spoiled; the patches of collard greens had dried up; the fish had disappeared because the river beds were dry. For true, hard times had come to Kaneh. Every day soft crying was heard because their hunger was great.

One day, as the village people sat silently in the sun, there came the sound of marching feet. Up the path came a column of loud-singing, hard-marching yams and cassava roots. The people took one look at this strange sight and ran to their houses and closed the doors. These were the "little devils" they had heard about. The yams marched all around the town, making all kinds of rude noise and shocking the people with their frisky dancing. After a time, they marched off down the path that led to the forest and disappeared.

From a crack in the door, Foday, the son of Famata, watched the strange doings. The "things" marching around did not look like "devils" to him. He kept his thoughts to himself, but early the next morning, Foday set his foot in the path that led to the forest. As he waited quietly on the dark path, along came the yams and cassava roots, marching and singing. Because there were so many of them, Foday was afraid and jumped behind a tree. From his hiding place, he watched them with hungry eyes. They looked like many roots he had eaten all of his life, so why shouldn't the people of Kaneh eat these things when their stomachs were so empty? Yet, Foday did nothing but stare at them.

As the column passed by, Foday caught sight of a big, fat yam, limping slowly, ever so slowly, far behind the others. "Ah-ha," said Foday, grabbing the yam by the head, "I will eat you if it kills me." The yam yelled and struggled, but Foday cut off his head and ran with him to his mother's cooking pot. Since there was nothing in the pot, he put the yam in the boiling water.

Foday sat nearby, watching the pot to see if the yam would do any witch business. After a time, Foday took the yam out and tasted it. It was sweet and delicious. He gave some to his mother and the rest of the family. They smacked their lips and licked their fingers. Everybody wanted to know where such fine food came from. Foday had to tell them how he had caught the yam and how foolish they were for thinking that yams were devils and unfit to eat. Here they were, sitting hungry, while food marched through their town.

The village people learned how to catch the "little devils," and they learned many ways to cook them. Back in the forest, the yams and cassava agreed that they must do something or else they would all be eaten up. So they decided to hide. Cassava suggested that they go inside the ground. That night every yam and cassava in the whole country dug a hole and buried himself, but that didn't stop the people. They took sticks and dug up the "little devils" and ate them.

Yams and cassava are still hiding underground, but they have become the favorite food along the coast of West Africa.

The yams marched all around the town

Hare Makes a Fool of Leopard

Leopard and Hare fell in love with Lady Deer, and both of them wanted to marry her.

Hare was walking in the forest with Lady Deer when Leopard came along. Lady Deer, who thought Hare was nothing but a "small boy," said haughtily, "Oh, I see my lover coming."

"Don't you love me?" asked Hare.

"No, I do not. Leopard is brave and strong, and you are not," replied Lady Deer.

"Leopard is a horse — a slave animal," said Hare.

"How can a leopard be a horse?" asked Lady Deer.

"He is my horse," angrily replied Hare. "He carries me on his back. He is my slave." Lady Deer did not believe him.

Hare went to Leopard for a secret talk. "I have been talking with Lady Deer, and she has sweet love for you, but she says she cannot marry such a fierce and terrible animal as you. I told her you had a tender and gentle heart, and I would prove it to her."

"I see," said Leopard. "Then we must prove that I am not what I am. Go on, Hare. What other things do you have to say?"

"My plan is this — you must be my horse and carry me through the town. Lady Deer will see us and think what a kind and gentle animal you are, and she will agree to marry you."

Leopard thought on Hare's plan and finally agreed to try it.

Hare tied a rope around Leopard's neck, jumped on his back and pretended to whip him like a horse. The next day Leopard went to see Lady Deer. He was shocked to hear her say, "Leave me, Leopard, you foolish animal. Hare told me you were his horse, his slave animal. Shame on you, Leopard. I will never speak to you again." Leopard realized he had been tricked by Hare, so off he rushed to find him. When Hare heard that Leopard was looking for him, he ran for two days, with Leopard right behind him.

At the end of the path was a cave that Hare knew.

Quickly he went and put his hands up to the ceiling as if he were holding it up. He waited until Leopard came in and cried out, "Take care, Leopard, the ceiling is falling down. Hold up this rock while I go for help or both of us will be crushed to death." Foolish, foolish Leopard pressed his paws against the ceiling with all his strength and Hare ran away.

Two raccoons came along and saw Leopard. "Brother Leopard," they asked, "why are you holding up a rock which was placed by God? Leave it, and come with us." Leopard saw that he had been tricked again, so he went with the raccoons.

A week later, Hare and his friend, Brother Giant Rat, caught the two raccoons. They took off the raccoons' skins and tied the two naked animals to a tree. In their new disguise, Hare and Brother Giant Rat went to Leopard's house. They were received as guests. After they had feasted, Leopard gave them a mat for sleeping. In the sleeping room was Mother Rat and her babies. She asked the guests to bring her some of Leopard's food. Hare agreed to do this for her, but Giant Rat protested such impudence. Mother Rat and her babies were so hungry that they ate the two coonskins while Hare and Giant Rat slept.

In the morning, Leopard knocked on the door of the guest room. No one opened the door or said, "Come." Leopard heard sounds inside. He peeped through a crack and saw a strange thing. There was Hare, running about the room looking inside pots and baskets, turning mats upside down and searching everywhere for something he could not find . . . and there was Giant Rat scrambling in a hole in the floor. The two raccoons who had entered the night before were nowhere to be seen.

Outside the room, Leopard began talking to himself. "I put two raccoons in that room and during the night they have turned into some other kind of thing. What kind of 'something' is this? For true, I do believe I see Hare and Giant Rat. This is indeed strange — I do not like Giant Rat a little bit and I don't like Hare at all!"

The more Leopard thought of this mischievous trick, the angrier he became. He showed his big white teeth and growled, "Wraaah, Wraaah!" He banged on the door. Still no answer. He broke down the door, but this time Hare had escaped through a hole in the floor with Giant Rat following him under the ground and out into the forest.

Leopard managed to grab Giant Rat's tail as he was running. Leopard pulled so hard that half the skin came off, but Rat got free and kept on running.

To this day Rat has a two-colored tail that makes him hide in dark holes for his shame.

Lady Deer heard of Hare's tricks and troubles and found them all very amusing. For his cleverness, she agreed to marry him. Because Leopard was rejected, he swore through his teeth to humbug Deer, Hare and Rat for the rest of his days. Even now he stalks them to get his revenge.

Zolu Dumah and the Priest

Chief Zolu Dumah ruled well the town of Gorn in the Vai-Kaneh chiefdom. He took seriously his task of protecting his people and their lands. The responsibilities of a chief are many, but the greatest one is to prevent war.

There was always the danger that spears would fly across the town in tribal war or rebellion, but thanks to Allah, during his reign as chief there had been no uprising or invasion. Still, he was uneasy. He wanted to make doubly sure that his chiefdom remained safe.

Chief Zolu sought the help of the Imam (Mohammedan priest). "Can you make magic strong enough to preserve my power?" He inquired of the priest. "There are sly enemies about me, and they may plot evil deeds against me. Can you prevent these things?"

The Imam nodded. "Oh Chief, the medicine can be made, and your power preserved."

"And can you make it so strong that I can overpower any rival who may rise up against me and my people? If you can do this, I will give you the greatest reward any man could wish," promised the Chief.

The priest was pleased to hear this, but dared not ask what his reward might be. He nodded his head again. "O Chief, with my skill and knowledge I can do all you ask."

Chief Zolu Dumah smiled much at the words of the priest, and praised himself in his own heart, saying, "Indeed, I am the cleverest of men, and for my cleverness my sons will rule a mighty kingdom. I will die with the blessings of my sons ringing in my ears."

The priest went away and labored long and hard to make the necessary medicine, and to make it strong enough to serve its appointed purpose. As he worked he wondered what his fine reward would be.

On the prescribed day for the working of the "medicine," the priest and Zolu went deep into the forest and stood in a shallow basket (rice fanner). Certain magic words were said by the priest that caused the fanner to rise in the air so high that Chief Zolu could see across the forest to the great rivers and mountains far, far away.

"O Chief," the priest cried, "you will rule till the end of your days over all the land that you see, and enemy spears will lose their power to hurt you."

When Chief Zolu returned to the ground in the fanner, he praised the priest: "O best of Imams, you have done a fine, fine thing. For this, you have my gratitude, and the devotion of my sons. But you must understand that I fear you may do some such thing for another chief. You may even work "medicine" on me — so I must kill you."

Zolu grabbed his spear and looked sternly at the priest. The priest looked steadily at the Chief.

"O faithless Chief, has all honor left you? Have you forgotten that you promised me the greatest reward that man could ask?"

"The greatest reward that any man can ask," replied the Chief, "is a sudden and clean death. What has gone before is lost; what comes ahead is unknown. A clean death is a painless birth into another life."

The Imam bowed his head in grief and disappointment, but he was a brave and holy man and felt that he had been betrayed. Just a "small dash" (a gift) would make his grief easier to bear. "O Chief, I beg your leave for a moment to pray."

"Then pray," replied the Chief.

The priest prayed to Allah, the All Highest. He prayed that Zolu might die slowly, and that no son of his might ever be chief. He raised his eyes after praying and said to Zolu, "I am ready."

Zolu, strong and mighty, struck the priest a shattering blow with his spear. The Imam fell to the ground dead.

Since that day no son of Zolu has ever been a chief, and no chief has come out of the town of Gorn with honor and a good name. And so it is with those who betray their words.

Zolu Dumah and the priest in the rice fanner

Tema's Promise
to the
White Bird

Tema lived in a fine town in Northern Liberia. He had no family, no land, no clothes to speak of, and not even a cooking pot. Since he had no family and not one friend, there was no one to tend or care for him. He begged for work but found none. He begged for food, but the people drove him from the village. Sadly he went to live in the bush. In a short time he became blind, and his hunger became great, for he had only small nuts and fruits to eat. When he thought he would surely die, he heard a voice calling to him, "Tema, Tema, if I help you, will you promise to help me?"

"Oh, yes," replied Tema, not knowing if he had heard a man's voice or the voice of a spirit.

The voice went on: "Lift your face up to the sky." Tema did so, and some hot, hot water fell in his blind eyes, and wah! His eyes were opened. He rubbed his eyes and looked to see where the voice was coming from, but he saw nothing.

"Close your eyes, Tema," said the voice. Tema did so. "Now open them."

Before him he saw a new town with new houses.

"This town is yours," the voice said.

"Thank you," said Tema, "but there are no people."

The voice commanded him to close his eyes again, and when he opened them, there were people, and goats, and children, all over the town. There were even pigeons and chickens, and also a few fat ducks.

"You will have ten wives, a hundred slaves, a thousand warriors and much gold. Go and live in the town and become its chief," the voice said. Tema's eyes were filled with tears at all this wealth. He looked down at his own rags and they had turned into the rich robes of a town chief.

Proudly, Tema walked into the fine, new town and began living in the biggest house with his ten wives around him and his servants to tend him.

He was happy, and as time passed his wives gave him many girl children and one boy child.

One day as Tema was out walking, he passed under a

giant cottonwood tree. From among its branches he heard a familiar voice call to him, "Tema, Chief Tema." He looked up and saw a big white bird.

"Tema," said the bird, "I helped you greatly once. Now I must ask your help." Tema agreed to help the bird, knowing in his heart that this was truly the one who had given him all of his good fortune.

"Come, here is my nest, and in it is one egg. I love this one egg very much, but I must leave it to go on a long journey. I want you to keep it from all harm while I am gone. You must love it and guard it as you would your only boy child." Tema willingly gave his word.

"If the egg should be boiled, spoiled or stolen, a strange and bad thing will happen to you," said the bird.

"Remember this, Tema — no bad thing must happen to this egg," said the big white bird and flew away.

Tema placed his bravest and strongest warriors to guard the bird's nest and went back to his house.

One fine day Tema's son, Siafa, was walking in the forest. He saw the nest up in the cottonwood tree and asked the servants to give him the egg. The servants refused, because Chief Tema had given them orders not to touch the special egg.

Siafa ran crying to his father, begging for the egg.

"No," said his father, "you may have a chicken egg, or a pigeon egg or a duck egg, but not that egg, for it does not belong to me. It belongs to my good friend and he asked me to guard it well."

Siafa wanted no other egg and began to wail and cry
foolishly. The father still refused. So Siafa refused to eat
his food and also refused to speak to his father.

Now, Tema loved his only son very much and it hurt
his heart to see his son vexed with him. Sadly, Tema
sent for his servants and told them to bring the egg.
Tema knew he was breaking his promise but he planned
to put the egg back after his son had looked at it. But not
so! The spoiled boy wanted the egg boiled. What a
shame!

Siafa was spoiled and petted by all the wives of Tema
and his own mother. So after the egg was boiled, he
didn't eat it, but threw it on the ground and smashed it
with his foot. How terrible! And what was poor Tema
to do?

Now, Tema did not know that the bird had also left a
little fly to watch the egg. The fly saw all that had happened and straightaway flew to the far-off place to report the happenings to the bird. The egg had been stol-
en, boiled and broken.

Sadly the big white bird flew back to the cottonwood
tree. It looked at the empty nest and then at Tema's fine
house. The sight of the empty nest made him cry for his
stolen egg. In a loud voice he called out to Tema:

"O weak and foolish Tema, you have broken your
word. You cannot keep a promise, for he who makes and
breaks a promise has not the right or might to be a chief.
So I will help you no longer."

As the big white bird flapped his wings Tema's blindness returned, his clothes turned to rags, the town disappeared and his tongue was twisted so he could not speak.

For a long, long time he wandered in the forest until he died.

The moral of this story is: Never make a promise unless you can keep it, and then you must keep it well.

Pakpai and Boto

One fine day Pakpai the turtle set his feet in the path that led to the forest. He was in a terrible vex. What caused the vex was this — Boto the jackal had stolen the meat of the bush hog Pakpai himself had caught in a trap.

As Pakpai walked along the path, muttering to himself, he came to a garden of banana trees. Bananas always made him hungry, so he began thinking of a way to get some of the fruit.

Up in a tree he saw a monkey eating bananas and Pakpai shouted, "Ho there, good friend! Throw me down some of those sweet bananas." The monkey looked down and said, "Climb up yourself and get your own fruit. Don't you know how to climb?" Now, everybody knows that a turtle can't climb a tree, but Pakpai said, "Oh yes, I can climb very well, but I am very tired just now." So, the monkey came down and put the turtle on his back and carried him up to the sweet bananas. The turtle ate and ate until his stomach was full to popping. Now he was ready to come down, but his friend, the monkey, had gone on with his family to a far tree over by the lake. Pakpai was up in the tree with no way to get down.

Down in the banana grove sat Boto the jackal. Jackals are not only roguish but greedy as well. Boto shouted loudly, "I am hungry, friend turtle. Fetch me down some of your fine fruit."

"Come close under the tree and open your mouth," said Pakpai. "Open your mouth wide and I will throw you some."

Turtle thought of a trick to play on the jackal, so he drew himself up tight and let himself fall hard on the jackal. This hard fall crushed Boto to death. Then Pakpai cut the leg of Boto open and took out his thighbone and made a fine whistle. He went to his house, playing this merry tune:

> The bone of the jackal makes me a flute
> twe, twe, twe,
> The bone of the jackal makes me a flute
> twe, twe, twe,
> The hair of the jackal makes me a suit
> twe, twe, twe,
> The life of the jackal has gone
> twe, twe, twe,
> The life of the jackal has gone
> twe, twe, twe.

As Pakpai whistled through the dark bush, the brother of the dead Boto heard the song and ran to find the turtle.

"What are you playing, my good friend?" asked the brother.

"I was playing: 'The bone of a *cow* makes me a flute, twe, twe, twe,' " said the turtle, for he was afraid of this evil brother. For sure, this one would eat Pakpai alive.

"No-o, that is not what I heard," said the brother.

"It must be because you are too close to me," said the frightened turtle. "Wait while I go over by that tree and you listen good." So the foolish jackal waited while the turtle went over to a cotton tree.

Beside the big tree was a large hole. In went the turtle. As soon as he was inside, he tuned up his whistle and played,

> The bone of a jackal makes me a flute
> twe, twe, twe,
> The bone of a jackal makes me a flute
> twe, twe, twe.

This made the jackal brother very angry and he ran to catch the turtle, but he could not reach him.

"I am going to dig you out," said the jackal. He saw a frog passing and said, "Stay, frog, and watch this hole while I fetch my digging things."

When the jackal had gone, the turtle came out of the hole and asked the frog, "Can you see me?"

"No," replied the frog, "it's too dark."

"Then open your eyes wider," said the turtle.

As the foolish frog opened his eyes wide, the turtle threw a portion of dirt into the frog's big eyes and quickly ran out of the hole.

The jackal came back and started digging at the hole. No turtle did he find. On and on he dug, but still no turtle did he find. In his anger he turned on the foolish frog and killed him.

From far away he heard the tune of the tricky turtle. It made him so angry that he tore himself in ten million pieces and that was the last of brother jackal.

To this very day jackals and turtles are not friends.

The Lady and the Devil

The Devil, who is an evil thing, lived far away in the deep dark forest. One day he caught a beautiful young girl who was walking on the forest path and carried her to his home.

Her brother heard of this terrible thing and was greatly vexed. He swore that he would not rest until he had found his sweet sister. Straightaway, he went to seek the help of the Head Medicine Man. The Medicine Man consulted his "medicine" and told him where the Devil could be found.

"Take these three eggs," said the Medicine Man, "and when danger is near, throw one on the ground until it breaks. You must do exactly that and no more." The

brother paid the Medicine Man his due and went to find
the path that led to the Devil's house. Here he found his
sister sitting on a rock, and beside her a big red rooster.

"O Sister," her brother cried, "come home with me.
Come now while the Evil One is away."

"Look, Brother," said the girl, "this rooster is here to
guard me from running away. If I move from this rock,
he will crow and the Evil One will return and do me
great harm."

Her brother reached in his coat and took one of the
eggs the Medicine Man had given him and threw it to
the ground. The egg was full of rice, and when it broke,
the rice scattered. The always-hungry rooster began to
eat.

While the rooster ate, the brother and sister quietly
ran down the path toward their home.

When the rooster saw that the girl was gone, he
crowed loudly and the evil Devil hurried home. Seeing
that the girl was surely gone, he started after them. As
they were crossing a bridge, the Devil came up behind
them and said, "A-ha!" Immediately the brother threw
another egg to the bridge, and the bridge fell into the
river, but this did not stop the Evil One.

The brother and sister ran on until they came to a big
old tree with a hole in it. They sat down to rest. Just as
they sat down they heard a weird noise coming out of
the hole in the tree.

The brother broke the last egg on the tree and out
came a small, small something with an orange head, long

teeth and red eyes. This small, small something had smelled the evil Devil nearby. He rushed at him and devoured him in time, thereby saving the sister and her brother.

They returned safely home and never again did the sister go into the forest alone. The moral of this story is: Never travel a dark path alone unless you know the path.

The Beginning of Spirit Societies

Once upon a time a certain man was walking through the forest and found a village where there were no people living — not a chicken, goat, dog or child. Every house was quiet and empty. For a very certain reason all the people had gone to another town. This certain reason we will tell you if you "wait small."

The man was tired when he reached the deserted village, so he went to find a house, for sleep was hard upon him. In order to make himself safe in this empty house, he climbed up to the thatched rafters under the roof and lay down.

While he was sleeping, a Gofe came into the house. A Gofe is an evil spirit belonging to a dead man. They are very scary-looking things and no man wants to come face to face with one of them.

More Gofes followed the first one, and soon the house was full of Gofes. They stood, sat and hung from every inch of the house. Unfortunately, this particular house was the meeting place for the Gofes of this town, and that is why all the people in the village had gone away.

The Gofes made so much noise with their spirit talk that it woke the man. He said to himself, This is a spirits' meeting and they want my life. I must escape before they find me. Down below in the house, more Gofes came. Some came in through the door and windows, others crept in through the cracks. The house was full of scary Gofes. They overflowed the house and sat on the roof and the trees nearby. Up in the rafters the man sat clutching his heart, for he was greatly afraid.

On the floor in the middle of the room, the Gofes opened their "medicine" bag and made a big dance around it, singing weird spirit songs. They did not know a man was in the house watching them.

The elder Gofes made big talk about the best way to avoid "Waras" and "Softlys." A Wara is a small, small animal that lives in a hollow log and makes scary noises at night. Nobody has ever seen a Wara, but they eat evil spirits. A Softly is an animal, small like a kitten, but with strong hands that can choke a big spirit. All evil spirits have a great fear of these two animals. Most of all they fear the voice of the Wara, which has the sound of a crying, dying thing.

The man sitting up under the roof began to plan his escape from this terrible situation. He cleared his throat and made a big shout — OOooo-Ow-Wa-ra-Wa-ra! This was a Wara kind of noise and sounded very much like a real Wara.

One of the Gofes in the room heard the noise and said, "I — think — I — heard — the — voice — of — something."

"What kind of something?" asked another Gofe. They trembled with fear, for the Wara is the most evil of spirits.

"It — was — the — call — of — a — Wara," said the elder Gofe. At these words every Gofe in the house turned pale with fright, and their wobbly knees turned to water.

"You are telling a black falsehood. It cannot be a Wara. Don't make such talk in here," said one.

"Then, let us listen good," said the first Gofe. They listened, and again the man made the terrible Wara sound.

"Yii-eeee! A Wara is upon us," cried all the Gofes. They ran every which way. They poured from the door and from the windows like rice from a bag. When they got outside, they melted and disappeared all at one time. Gofes can melt and slide away quick, quick, and no eyes can see them. They left in such a big hurry that they forgot their medicine bag. This bag was full of all kinds of things — bones, stones, feathers, sticks, seeds, and strange shells.

All through the night the man stayed up in the ceiling, listening for the return of the Gofes.

When daylight came, the man came down and found

the medicine bag where the Gofes had left it. He took it to his house, and, because his fear of evil spirits was still upon him, he built a strong fence to keep out all strangers.

On a special day the man invited certain members of his clan to share the secrets of the Gofes medicine bag. Some of the medicine they made proved very evil, and some of it made good things happen. The proof of the medicine was in the mind of the believer — and that was how the Spirit Societies began.

How a Wuuni Ate Nine Evil Spirits

An evil spirit lived in a hole in the ground as evil spirits do. He had a wife and seven children. Hunger was sitting hard in the spirit's house. The children cried, "Father, find us something to eat or we will die." So the evil father went out to see what he could find.

Down the path he met a man who was carrying a bag of rice on his head. "Old man," said the evil spirit, "we are going the same way. Let me help you carry your load. Place it on my head while you rest." The tired old man, not recognizing the evil spirit for what he was, readily agreed.

The Evil One started off with the rice on his head, but he walked so fast that the man could not keep up with him. So, into the dark forest ran the evil spirit with the man's rice. As he got near his home, he began to sing:

> Put on the pot and make it hot,
> To cook what I am bringing,
> I bring a prize, a fine surprise,
> Which makes a song for singing.

The evil spirit mother cooked the rice, and the family ate until their stomachs were full.

Each day the Evil One went on the path to find persons who were carrying parcels of food. He always managed to trick someone out of his load. In this manner he fed his family. He was too lazy to grow his own food and too roguish to buy any. So he continued to steal from people until they became so vexed that they went to the Head Mawni and complained against the spirit. They wanted the evil spirit banished from their town.

In the Loma tribe, the Mawni society is very important and very secret, and the Head Mawni in each town owns at least one "Wuuni." A Wuuni is a thing you can't see, coming or going, and it has no respect for evil spirits. The Wuuni is such strong "medicine" that the Mawni calls on it only when the trouble is very great.

The Head Mawni talked to his Wuuni with many secret words, and then he put the Wuuni in a bag of rice. He put the bag on his head and went walking down the path, singing loudly. The evil spirit heard the singing

and offered to help the Mawni with his heavy load. The
Evil One took the load and ran to his house singing:

> A bag of rice is rather nice,
> And better if it's stolen,
> Let's fill the pot and eat the lot,
> Until we are fully swollen.

The Wuuni inside the bag of rice laughed quietly,
which made a fearful cool wind slip down the evil spirit's
back. Inside the bag the Wuuni began to sing softly:

> An evil thing should never sing,
> While bearing bags untied,
> They might have mice instead of rice,
> Or something worse inside.

The evil spirit gave the Wuuni his children one by
tied the Mawni's bag of rice and — Wah! — out jumped
the Wuuni. The children screamed and ran to hide in
the bush. "GIVE ME FOOD," said the Wuuni. The evil
spirit had no food, so he threw his wife to the Wuuni.
What a choice morsel! He tore her into many pieces and
cracked her bones.

"MORE, MORE," cried the Wuuni.

The evil spirit gave the Wuuni his children one by
one, and he ate them all and cracked their bones. When
the Wuuni finished all the children, the evil spirit tried
to make himself small so that the Wuuni wouldn't devour
him. The Wuuni looked at him and sang:

You have stolen, lied and cheated,
All those who do such things,
Must be badly treated.

The Wuuni did not eat the evil spirit at once, because
the Head Mawni had asked him to bring the rogue back
to town.

This evil spirit was the undead part of a man who had
died in the town some years past, and everybody wanted
to find out why he had been doing so many bad things
instead of helping with the farm work.

Whenever anyone is accused of a bad deed, it is the
custom to have a trial. A two-room house was selected
for the ceremony. The family of the dead man gathered
in one room, and the Head Mawni, the Wuuni and the
evil spirit entered the other room, which was empty
except for a few dry sticks.

The Head Mawni asked the spirit why he had been so
wicked since he had departed his mortal body.

"My family gave me a hard time," the spirit answered.
"I told them my spirit would humbug them when I died,
but they laughed. They made me suffer many hard
things. Then, when I died, they passed my grave and
never looked back. This is hard for a man to bear."

His family and descendants in the next room grew
vexed and together they talked of their kindness to him
during his natural life. They could hear the Wuuni saying in his nasal voice, "LET ME KILL HIM."

There was much palaver between the people in the

two rooms, but it was finally decided that the evil spirit must die for his roguish ways. The Head Mawni left the job of killing the evil spirit to the Wuuni.

The family in the next room heard the sounds of eating and the cracking of bones. Then, all was quiet.

Later, they went in, after the Wuuni had gone away. Not a speck or morsel was on the floor to show the passing of the evil spirit. In the center of the room sat the Head Mawni and beside him a few dry sticks.

The evil spirit never returned to humbug the town and its people. Thus an evil spirit suffered a terrible end and justice was done, as it always is with liars, rogues and cheats.

How Monkey King Became a Slave

When the world was filled with all kinds of animals, there were many animal kings. Because the monkeys were so foolish and disobedient, the great Sky God gave them a special king name Quilpu-nine. This King Quilpu-nine was a bird with ugly gray hair all over his body and small red eyes. He made his home in a hole in the ground where no one could see him.

The monkey people were afraid of this strange thing in the hole and not a soul would go near it. Its voice was so loud and frightening that the people thought it was some powerful devil god. So, all the monkeys obeyed and respected King Quilpu-nine.

It was the rule and custom in that day that all animals pay proper respect to their king by giving him the best fruit, the sweetest nuts and the choicest leaves to eat. In this way Quilpu-nine grew fat and lazy.

As the rains came and went, so did hungry times come to the forest. The long, hot dry season had ruined many of the fruit and nut trees, and there was only a little food to be found. There was much hunger among the animals. Since there were no choice things to bring the King, he grew lean and thin. His hunger was too much for him. So one day, while the monkey fathers were away looking for food, the King crept out of his hole and stole the small food from the monkey children's pots.

When the monkey mothers and fathers came back, they were surprised to find the children laughing and poking sticks into the King's hole in the ground.

"Ma," they said, "he is not a king. He is just an old gray bird who stole our kola nuts."

The monkey fathers were so vexed that they pulled him from his hole and made him their slave. They beat him with sticks and mocked him with many bad words. Even now you can hear the monkey people laughing in the forest, for they can remember when they believed a foolish bird was their king.

The Lizard and the Catfish

A lizard with an orange-colored head lived in a certain tree close to the river. More than anything in the world he wanted to marry, but he wanted a wife with soft, smooth skin. Now, in the river lived a fine catfish who had soft, smooth skin. This fine catfish wanted to marry someone with an orange-colored head.

One day a woodcutter came into the forest and cut down the tree in which the lizard lived, and the tree fell near the river. Lizard walked along the fallen tree and looked down into the water. There he saw Catfish with her soft, smooth skin; and Catfish looked up and saw Lizard with his bright orange head. They fell in love.

Catfish invited Lizard to come down to her home in the bottom of the river, where it was cool and muddy.

82

Lizard accepted the invitation and went down to the bottom of the river to visit with Catfish. Poor Lizard was very uncomfortable in this cool, dark place. Everybody knows a lizard likes heat and bright sunlight, but his love for the smooth, soft skin of the catfish made him enter the river. He nearly died from the cold and dampness.

In the morning, Lizard invited Catfish to his home on the stump of a tree, and she accepted. Poor Catfish nearly died on that hot, dry stump. The sun burned her soft skin, and she begged Lizard to take her back to the river.

So the two agreed that marriage between them was impossible. From that time on they have lived in their own homes, which shows that people should look for more than beauty when they seek to marry.

He Danced Fine-O

Jobai was a young boy of the Vai tribe who lived with his two older sisters in the town of Bendaja. His mother and father were dead and the sisters treated him cruelly. For dinner and supper he was given the scraps that the sisters did not eat.

The girls were ashamed of their brother because he had many sores and scabs all over his feet and legs. Because of their shame, Jobai was abused and given much hard work to do. Whenever there was a feast in a nearby town the sisters were always invited to come and dance. For all their meanness, the sisters were very good dancers. Little brother would always beg to go with them, but they would beat him and give him more work to do.

Jobai danced too too fine

Each time his sisters left for a feast, Jobai would take off his sores and scabs and hide them. Then he would change into a handsome young man and go to the feast. After dancing and feasting, he would run home and put on his sores and scabs again.

When his sisters returned, they were surprised to find that Jobai knew everything that had happened at -the feast.

"How do you know all these things?" they asked.

"Well," replied Jobai, "I fell asleep while you were gone and dreamed of the great feast. In my mind's eye I saw it all."

The sisters did not believe him and abused him with many cross words.

One day an old lady came to the house begging for food. The cruel sisters drove her from the door, but Jobai gave her his small food. On this same day a feast was being held in the next town. Again, Jobai begged his sisters to let him go. They ignored him and went off to dance at the feast.

Just as soon as they were out of sight, Jobai took off his sores and scabs and put them in a secret place. Then he slipped away to the feast. The old woman had been watching him and saw where he hid the ugly sores. With a small pile of dry sticks, she burned the sores and scabs and threw the ashes in the river.

Back at the feast, the sisters saw a handsome young man who danced better than anyone else. They watched him with love in their eyes. After a little while they went up to him and told him of their love and begged him to marry them. "Wait small," he said. "As soon as the feast is over we will talk the marriage palaver." He knew he would not be there until the end of the feast.

Jobai's dancing was so fine that the people "dashed" him with a sheep, a goat, a cow, palm oil and rice. He took all the gifts home with a happy heart. Immediately, he went to find the old lady. He said, "I have brought you all these fine gifts, for you are old and poor and for all my thoughts you might have been my mother. So, old woman, you must take all these things and go quickly. My sisters might take your things and beat you for being here. Go good, old woman."

When Jobai went to find his sores he discovered they were gone. He looked in all his secret places, but he could not find even a tiny sore. Behind him the old woman said, "Do not look anymore. I have burned those ugly things and the ashes are in the river. For true, I am the spirit of your mother, my son, and you will be blessed a hundred times for your kind and loving ways. As for your wicked sisters, they will never find their way back to this house." With these words the old lady disappeared.

Jobai looked at his gifts and they had multiplied. His one sheep had become a hundred sheep and the same thing happened to the cow and the goat. Now he was a rich man with many cattle and much rice, but Jobai did not change his kind and loving ways. He went far into the forest looking for his sisters and calling loudly to them. Although they could hear his voice, they could never find the path to the house, and no one could say where they had gone.

Moral: Cruel deeds have their own reward.

How People Became Different

Once upon a time there lived a great warrior who fought so many battles in so many kingdoms that his empire covered almost all of the west side of Africa.

The name of this great and powerful warrior was Amata Kepaka. The people thought so highly of his great deeds that they made him their king.

Throughout the kingdom the name of Amata Kepaka was feared and respected. Whenever he passed through the cities and villages, men bowed their heads and the women and children hid their faces.

Amata had many, many wives (about three hundred) and many, many slaves. All of them served the King and his household well. His wives gave him many fine, strong sons, but the King longed for a girl child to bless his old age.

Time passed, and Hawa, the youngest wife of King Amata, presented him with a beautiful baby girl. The baby was so fine that people came from far, far places to look on her beauty. The years passed and the girl grew into a beautiful princess with many admirers.

Her father was now an old man and wished for his daughter to take a husband before he died.

Four handsome warriors heard of the beautiful princess and decided to ask for her hand in marriage. They gathered many fine presents and sent them to the King by a special messenger. The old King thought well of the gifts but was afraid to give his daughter to any one of the warriors, for it might cause the others to start a war against his kingdom. So he called the witch doctors and medicine men to him, and asked them for a plan he could use to get a suitable husband for his daughter.

The Head Doctor with the strongest "medicine" asked the King to give him a dog, a rooster, a cat and his daughter. For a moment the King hesitated, but he finally agreed to give the medicine man all he asked for. He took the animals and the girl to his house, far away in the forest.

For seven days the Head Doctor talked to his secret spirits and performed many sacrifices and tricks. These tricks turned the dog, the rooster and the cat into girls who looked just like the real princess. Then the Doctor took all of them to the King.

"But how," asked the King, "do I see four girls instead of my one?"

"Your eyes do not deceive you — what you see is truly so," replied the medicine man.

The King was so impressed with this magic that he straightaway gave him a large portion of land in the northern part of his kingdom.

The King now sent for the four young warriors, saying that they could send their dowries according to the law and custom. The custom in this land was for a rich man to send goats, cattle or gold to the bride's father. The more he sent, the more impressed the bride's people would be. According to his wealth, each warrior sent two hundred bags of gold and ten head of cattle.

After the proper ceremonies the King sent the three "animals turned girls" and his own daughter to become wives to the warriors.

Some years after their marriages, each of the girls gave birth to a son. When the news reached the King he was not pleased, because he did not know which girl was his real daughter or which son was his real grandson. In order to find out the truth, he decided that each grandson should come and spend some time at his court.

The first boy came and was royally welcomed to the court with much music, dancing and feasting. After the feast, the King invited him to walk along the palace path with him. While they were walking, the King asked the boy about his home affairs. The boy replied politely, "My father is kind and loving to my mother, but she is very inquisitive and always meddling in other people's affairs." From this answer the King knew this boy was the son of the dog changed into a girl and not his true grandson. He was sent away.

At another time, the old King invited the second grandson to come and visit him. This grandson was also given a fine welcome and a grand feast. Again the King took this boy along the path and asked him about his home affairs. Eagerly, the boy replied, "My father is good to my mother, but she treats him very badly. She is very frisky, and causes much 'palaver' in the village. Her nose is too much in everybody's business."

"What is the palaver your mother is causing?" asked the King. "Well," said the boy, "she steals small, small things from the people." Sadly, the King shook his head, for he knew this boy was the son of the cat turned girl. This boy was also sent away.

The third grandson came to visit the King and was also welcomed in a royal manner. He was asked about his home. He said his father loved his mother very much, but she did not care for him and was spending much time with other men in the town. From this, the King knew this boy was the son of the rooster turned girl.

At long last the fourth grandson was given the opportunity to visit the King's palace. He told the King, "My mother does everything to make my father happy but he treats her like dirt. Many times her eyes are filled with sad tears," For true, the King knew this was his real grandson and his mother was his true daughter. This

Devil dancers entertaining at the feast for the first grandson

knowledge gave the King great pleasure, for now he could die in peace.

The old King thought on how each son was different according to his mother, and so from that time on there have been different kinds of people. Each kind has some of his father and most of his mother in him. Look at your friends and see.

Disobedient Hawa

A fine girl called Hawa and her junior brothers lived with their family at the edge of a small town. This was a poor town and everyone worked hard to get food.

The mother of Hawa made fish traps and set them in the river nearby. But as she grew old and her hands grew stiff, she told Hawa to continue her work.

The river where the mother put her fish traps was indeed a strange place. Many terrible devils made their home in the river. So the chief told the people of the village not to go to this particular river to catch fish, for many women had been caught by the devils who lived in the water. Hawa's mother warned her against taking fish from this river or even putting her foot in the river. Hawa agreed to keep her mother's words.

Now hungry time came to the village, and Hawa looked on her junior brothers and her old mother in their hunger, and it gave her a terrible sadness. So Hawa took the canoe and the fish traps and went down the river.

She looked about — the water was quiet, with only the beautiful silver and blue fish jumping in and out. She decided to throw her fish net across the quiet river. This she did, and caught so many fish that the net was too heavy for her to pull in while standing in the canoe. Hawa stepped out of the boat with the ends of the net in her hand so she could drag the net to the shore.

Just as she stepped into the river, the water began to rise up to her neck. She yelled and screamed. No one came to help her; only a night bird flying by hovered over her. She sang to him:

> Bird on your journey tonight,
> Visit my house,
> Tell my mother you saw me out of sight.

As the water continued to rise, Hawa continued to sing:

> Tell her I remember her words,
> But my head was hard,
> Yet my heart was soft with love.

No sooner had she finished singing, than the water began to go down, and there stood Hawa on dry ground with a net full of fine fish.

Hawa carried the fish home, and never did her mother know that her disobedience had kept hunger from their house one time.

The Anger of Sande-Nyana

Once upon a time (the listeners repeat the word *time*), three brothers lived in a small village near Lake Piso. The brothers were called Khamah, Vaani and Zuke.

Early one morning they went into the forest to hunt. With them they took their spears and small "chop" (food). They walked to a far place they had never been before. Here they found a sacred thing, a Gnomaneah (a small stone figure used in certain tribal ceremonies) and close beside it a bag of gold.

"It is the scared shrine of Sande-Nyana," said Khamah. He was terribly afraid and looked about with scared eyes. Now, everyone in the country knows that Sande-

Nyana is the women's devil god, and is dangerous and cruel if disrespected.

"Sande is not here, and the Gnomaneah is old and of no use any more. The village is empty and the people are gone," said Vaani. He was shaking all over with fear. All three brothers knew that the power of Sande-Nyana was great enough to kill them dead one time.

"But the gold, the beautiful, sweet gold," said Zuke. "Look at all the fine pieces. Let us each take one." Khamah took one piece and said to Zuke, the junior brother, "Take this gold piece to the village and buy us some wine. We will wait under the tree."

The two brothers waited under the cotton tree, thinking of that bag of gold beside the Gnomancah and all the wine, all that gold would buy. Fear of the anger of Sande-Nyana kept them from taking more than one piece.

In the village, Zuke bought a calabash of wine. As he walked along with the wine, Evil came into his head and told him to put poison in the wine and give it to his brothers. Upon their death he could take the bag of gold for himself. So he stopped and picked a few poison leaves and crushed them in the wine. As he continued walking with the poisoned wine, his brothers back at the tree were also planning to do evil to Zuke when he returned.

They said, "Let us kill our younger brother when he returns with the wine. Then we can have the gold for ourselves."

Zuke came with the wine and put it on the ground. Vaani and Khamah took their spears and struck him dead. Then they sat down and drank the wine that was filled with strong poison. Thus, Vani and Khamah died for their evil deed.

All three brothers were greedy for gold and did evil deeds to gain possession of it. But none has ever taken the bag of gold from the shrine of Sande-Nyana, for her power is too great for human man.

How Dog Came to Live with Man

All the animals in the forest agreed to hold a feast, and everyone was invited. Now Leopard has always been the enemy of Dog, and at this great feast he objected to the idea of Dog's being invited. He said, "Dog is the eater of bad things. He is a wicked and unclean animal. He has no manners and will only shame himself if he eats with others who are polite."

The other animals did not agree, so Dog was invited to the feast. When the dog was ready and all the distinguished animals had been seated, Leopard slipped into the kitchen and told the cook not to give Dog a bone, but to give him a bowl of soup. Dog drank the soup with much noise, because he was not accustomed to drinking soup. Leopard sat down beside Dog with a nice, juicy bone. He smacked his lips and made appreciative noises.

When he saw Dog watching him, he took the chance to shame him in public. Leopard threw his bone up in the air. Dog jumped up to catch it, not looking where he jumped, and stepped in many dishes of food, spilling them on the table. When he got the bone, he scrambled over Possum and Hare and ran away to eat the bone. The other animals were shocked and surprised and hung their heads in shame. Leopard was happy because he had shamed Dog. "I told you so. Dog has no manners and should not join our feasting again."

All the animals abused Dog with many harsh words. Because of this, Dog had no friends in the forest. He grew lonely and hungry. He left the forest and went to the nearest village. Outside the house where Man lived there were many fine bones. No one drove him away or shamed him as he ate. So Dog remained near Man's house and there he has been ever since.

All About the Tail of the Leopard

Clever, greedy Leopard likes to eat monkeys and is forever planning tricks to catch them.

One fine day, as Leopard lay in a cool place resting himself, he thought of a clever trick that would bring him much monkey meat. He thought he would make friends with all the monkey families so he could eat them all one by one.

Now, this tricky Leopard was growing old and could not climb much. He went to the palm tree where the Monkey Chief sat eating fruit with his wives and little ones. Very politely Leopard said, "Good day, Chief. How are you feeling? If it pleases you, let us make talk."

Monkeys don't trust leopards, so as Leopard came to
make talk, the monkeys climbed to the top of the tree
where the branches were thin — too thin to hold a big
leopard. From there the monkeys threw fruit and bad
words at Leopard. He dodged the fruit and ignored the
bad words.

"I came in peace, my good friend," said Leopard. "In
my young days I was wild and savage but now I am old
and soon will die. Before I die I want to make friends
with all my enemies. I wish to live with you, my good
friends, and learn your jumping "medicine." His greedy,
yellow eyes looked on the Monkey Chief's fat wife. She
trembled with fear and hid behind the Chief.

"Your words are sweet, but your old yellow teeth are
still sharp," said the Monkey Chief. "This must be con-
sidered by our council. Come tomorrow and we will see."

Before Leopard came on the next day, Monkey Chief
hid one of his small children inside a palm basket and
fastened it tight. He put the basket on the ground under
the plum tree. When Leopard came, Monkey Chief told
him, "O friendly Leopard, take this basket to your house,
but do not open it. This is a test to see if we can trust
you. Bring the basket back tomorrow. If you have not
opened it, we will show you our jumping medicine and
then you may live with us."

Greedy Leopard took the basket to his house with
happy heart. That night he and his wife talked of nothing but how they would feast on monkey meat and

grow fat. The little monkey inside the basket heard and remembered all that was said.

When morning came, Leopard carried the basket back to the plum tree. Monkey Chief opened the basket, and Little Monkey told his father all the evil words he had heard from Leopard and his wife. Monkey Chief suspected some trick, for Leopard is wicked and has no true friends.

With two strong wives, Monkey Chief climbed down to a branch near the ground and said, "Leopard, if you live with us, you must eat the food we eat. Can you eat this banana?" He threw a banana to Leopard. He smelled it and knew it was not leopard food, but he swallowed it down, skin and all. Then Monkey threw him a plum. Leopard bit it and broke one of his big teeth on the hard plum seed. He pretended nothing had happened and swallowed plum, tooth and seed.

Next, Monkey Chief threw him a hot chili pepper. It set Leopard's mouth on fire. Tears ran from his eyes, so hot was the pepper.

"O Leopard," said Monkey, almost bursting with laughter, "I see you cannot eat monkey food. Now we must show you our jumping medicine. To jump and swing as monkeys do, you must learn to use your tail. Raise it so, and we will show you how this thing is done." Leopard raised his tail. As he did so, Monkey and his wives grabbed it. In an instant they had pulled Leopard into the air and tied his tail to a branch. Then all the monkeys

threw plums and insulting words at Leopard as he swung
in the tree by his tail.

> Swing, swing, O Leopard, swing
> Your false tale has earned you
> A crooked tail.

When you look on Leopard, you will see that his tail
swings from right to left when he is angry. He still re-
members the monkeys he didn't eat.

The Three Who Made Ku

Once upon a time, Leopard, Man and Dog made "ku." That is, they agreed to bring, for all to eat, meat that was fresh and sweet to the taste, and if any member of the ku broke the agreement by not bringing a portion of meat, he would be punished by his ku brothers.

Whenever a ku is made, each member has a day to gather the things to pay his ku. Man, Leopard and Dog each had a day to pay their ku. The first one to be called on was Leopard. He went into the forest and killed a bush hog. While Leopard was hunting, Man and Dog were busy clearing the bush to make a farm. When Leopard had cooked the hog, he called Man and Dog to come and eat. Before eating, both of them scratched the meat to see if it was fresh. For true, the meat was fresh, sweet and tender, and all three ate their stomach's full.

After cutting some more bush for the farm, Leopard said to Dog, "Let us show Man a day to bring his ku." Man did not agree to pay his ku just now. So Leopard and Man showed Dog a day, but Dog said they must give him two days to hunt for his ku. They agreed, and Dog went to the forest. He killed a red deer and carried it to Man and Leopard.

"My ku people," said Dog, "here is something to eat with the cassava. It is sweet and tender." Leopard scratched the meat and found it fresh, so they cooked it with boiled cassava and ate their stomachs full. Man and Leopard went back to cut more farm while Dog hunted the second day. This time Dog made a big hunt; he killed one black deer and another bush hog. When he brought the meat, Leopard tested it and then they ate until their stomach's were full.

As they continued to clear away more bush for their farm, hunger came to them, so Dog turned to Man and said, "You, my good friend, will have two days to pay your ku." Man trembled. "No, no, two days are not enough," he said. "Show me four days, I beg you." Dog stamped his foot and yelled loudly, "No, no, no! I had only two days and Man should have the same." With one look at Dog, Leopard quietly said, "Man shall have three days." Dog was very vexed but he said nothing, for Leopard was the big member of the ku. So Dog tucked his tail, and Man put his foot in the path to the forest.

The old woman gave Man a bush cow horn

Man set his traps and waited. The first day passed and Man caught nothing. The second day Man went farther into the forest and set his trap. At sundown, the trap was still empty. Fear came and sat on Man's heart, for now he had only one more day left to get meat to pay his ku. He knew what the big penalty would be if he did not bring fresh meat to Leopard and Dog.

Not knowing what to do, Man stopped at a palm tree nearby and began cutting palm nuts to ease his fear. An old lady heard him cutting and asked, "What are you doing?" "Cutting nuts, old woman," answered Man.

"Come," said the woman, "take the cutlass and cut the bush around my hut."

"Old woman," replied Man, "I would gladly oblige you, but I am in ku with Leopard and Dog. They gave me three days to pay my ku and two days are already finished and my trap is empty. I beg you to excuse me this time, old woman, for I must catch meat today or I will meet my end for true. A ku must be kept, and my time is short."

"Cut the grass, my man. You never know what can bless you," said the old woman. Because of her age and her wise, wise words, Man took the cutlass and cleared the bush from around the hut. The shadow of the sun told him the time was getting late for him. Again fear sat heavy on his heart.

The old woman looked on his sad face and said, "Never mind ya. You have done well for me, I will do well for you." From a bag tied around her waist, the old woman took a bush cow horn and gave it to Man. "In this horn there is black powder that has a powerful magic. When you go in the forest, you will see a black deer. Point the horn at him and say, 'I kill you.' The deer will fall dead one time." While the old woman was talking, Man was watching his powerful gift with anxious eyes. Suppose the horn failed? How would he pay his ku? He thanked her and went into the forest. The first animal he saw was a black deer. He pointed the horn with the black powder in it at the deer and said, "I kill you." The deer fell dead. Quickly, Man took the deer to the old woman because she had given him the power to kill meat without a trap. She would have sweet meat for her family. Back to the forest went Man to get his ku meat.

Far away at the new farm, Dog was making talk with Leopard. "Let us catch Man and eat him. He cannot catch meat to pay his ku." Leopard did not answer him, for he was thinking other thoughts.

Soon Man came. Dog mocked and scolded him for keeping them waiting two days. "Hold your tongue, Dog," said Man. "I bring a bush hog, two black deer and three red deer. This can be our ku meat for today. Come, let us cook and eat." Leopard scratched the meat, and then they ate until their stomachs were full. As the moon came up in the sky, Dog said, "Let us go to a secret place where we can talk business." When they reached a far place in the forest, Dog turned to Man and Leopard and said, "Let us show to each other the things we use to kill meat." Leopard jumped to a tree and scratched it with his sharp claws. "This is what kills my meat," bragged Leopard as he continued to tear the tree to pieces. Dog ran to a tree and bit it with his sharp teeth. "This is what I use." He ripped the bark from the tree in long wide gashes, proving that his teeth were indeed sharp. Now it was Man's turn to show what he used to kill meat. "Leopard," he said, "the thing I have is bad and its power is evil."

"Show it to us so we may know this evil thing," begged Leopard. Man backed away from them. "No, no, don't beg me to show you this thing, for it is evil beyond all things."

Leopard and Dog came and stood before Man and said, "If you don't show it to us, we will kill you and eat you right here."

Sadly, Man looked at them and said, "I do not wish to die for ku business, so I will show it to you." Man quietly pointed the horn with black powder in it at Leopard. With the words *I kill you*, Leopard fell dead. Dog shook with fear. His skin shivered and his tail dropped. He crawled up to Man, begging him not to kill him. He begged with his eyes and wagged his tail. Man had pity on him, but told him sternly, "I will not kill you, but from now on you must eat your own ku and I will eat mine, for Man, Dog and Leopard were not made to eat ku together."

To this day, dog begs man and wags his tail when his ku meat is given and eaten, and never again have Dog and Man made ku business together.

LIBERIAN PROVERBS

A borrowed drum is hard to beat.
(If you beat it too hard, you will spoil it and have to pay
  for it; if you don't beat it hard, the dancers won't
  hear it.)

You can't spill water and pick it up again.
(What you have said cannot be taken back.)

An invited guest does not eat crab.
(Prepare the feast before you invite the guest.)

A rooster cannot crow in his neighbor's town.
(You cannot do in another town what you can do in your
  own.)

Tame and wild animals are hit with different sticks.
(Friendship and blood alter arrangements.)

You sew it loosely, you wear it loosely.
(A poorly cut farm will grow poor crops.)

He who pierces his own heart can pierce his thigh.
(If you are cruel to your kin, you can be cruel to anyone.)

Cassava leaf is not for goat alone.
(Big man or small boy can eat country "chop.")

When Leopard is not in the forest, the deer are frisky.
(The children play when the elders are away.)

Joke is joke and play is play, but putting your finger in a
    dead man's eye is cheeky.
(Don't tease, if you cannot take the punishment.)

Blood in body and water in heart.
(Strong men do not always perform big deeds.)

Small axe can cut down big tree.
(Truth can outlive big lies.)

You can bend a young stick but not a cottonwood tree.
(Train a child when he is young.)

Empty pots make a lot of noise.
(Little people with small, small things pretend they have
more.)

Women are like a cassava stick with many eyes.
(Women look around for more than one man.)

A monkey's hand is always black.
(Once a rogue, always a rogue.)

Any kind of water puts out a fire.
(To some extent, anything satisfies a need in some
degree.)

Sitting comes before waking or sleeping.
(Everything happens in sequence.)

No one puts two cook spoons in his mouth at the same
time.
(Do not eat from two different houses at the same meal.)

When deceit climbs a tree, brush the undergrowth.
(Wait for dishonesty to come to light.)

If your own knife cuts you, throw it down and pick it up
again.
(If your blood kin harms you, forgive him, but watch him
ever after.)

Big-boy shoes, small boy can't wear.
(An untrained person cannot take a big job.)

Palm nuts do not grow on plum trees.
(Everything has a place and a season.)

One tree does not make a forest.
(It takes many people to elect a chief.)

Do not send a cat to take of dry fish.
(If you know a man is a rogue, do not give him the keys
   to your house.)

The forest you overlook is the place the rope will come
   from to tie you up.
(The person you bypass or condemn might be the one
   to help you in the future.)

If a rogue comes to you, invite him in, but if a liar comes
   to you, turn him away.
(Thieves take things that can be replaced, but the tales
   of a liar hurt for life.)

Big heads make little talk, and little heads make big
   mouth.
(An important man keeps quiet, while an ignorant man
   makes a fool of himself.)

Softly, softly, catches monkey.
(Kind words can make more friends than a pot of rice.)

Two captains can't steer a ship; neither can one captain
    steer two ships.
(One chief can rule a tribe, but two would cause a war.)

Wounded birds only flutter.
(When one is sorely hurt, no cry is made; the foolish
    ones make loud sounds.)

A man with long fingernails does not get craw-craw.
(The clever man uses what he has to make life better.)

Hunger makes monkey eat pepper.
(When things are very bad, you will do anything to
    make them better.)

You send monkey, monkey sends its tail.
(Never send by mouth what you can send by letter.)

If you have no rope, you cannot tie a parcel.
(Without cleverness you cannot get the important posi-
    tion.)

The big man is the servant of the small boy.
(The educated person makes right what the untrained
    person did wrong.)

When a snake enters a crooked hole, it should be taken
out with a crooked stick.
(It takes a crooked person to find a crooked person.)

When frog was young she didn't sweat; when she is old,
the sweat will come.
(When a girl is young and doesn't care for clothes and
lovemaking, she will seek these things when she is old.)

Ugly people go for water, but do not take a big bucket.
(A petty thief is the first one to say he is not guilty. He
proves his ugliness at once.)

The noise of the guinea fowl is the same whether it's
flying up or down.
(False laughter is the same wherever you hear it.)

If your legs are short, do not try to kick.
(Bring good common sense if you want to change something.)

Small peanuts are not slaves to big ones.
(Everybody is equal, regardless of size.)

Family stick can bend but it cannot break.
(Relatives may have harsh words but they will stay on
good terms.)

One man can't drink a creek dry.
(It takes more than one person to do a big piece of work.)

Water is sweet when the weather is dry.
(You never realize the good things until it's too late.)

What is fun to a small boy is death to a frog.
(When you hurt someone, you never realize how serious
    it can be.)

Pepper is not painful on sores.
(Do the same to others as you would have them do to
    you.)

A note about the editor

Edythe Rance Haskett is a teacher from Norfolk, Virginia. She recently returned from West Africa where she had spent two years teaching at the Episcopal High School, in Robertsport, Liberia. During that time she collected the stories told in this book.

A note about "Musu Miatta"

The Vai name Musu Miatta was given to me by members of my art classes, who felt that during my two years with them I had been more than a teacher. In the Vai language, *Musu* means mother, or woman, and *Miatta* means kind or beloved. To be thus honored is a rare privilege bestowed upon a select few who sojourn in the beautiful land of the Vai people. To see truth (sincerity) in the eyes of the *kwi* (foreigner) is a fine thing, but to clasp the hand and share the heart is truly a fine, fine thing.

EDYTHE RANCE HASKETT